TASTING FREEDOM

THE NINE LIVES OF GABRIELLE: FOR THREE SHE PLAYS - BOOK 3

LAURA MARIANI

the
PEOPLE
ALCHEMIST

CONTENTS

ABOUT THE AUTHOR

Laura Mariani is an Author, Speaker and Entrepreneur.

She started her consulting business after a successful career as Senior HR Director within global brands in FMCG, Retail, Media and Pharma.

Laura is incredibly passionate about helping other women to break through barriers limiting their personal and/or professional fulfilment. Her best selling nonfiction *STOP IT! It is all in your head* and the *THINK, LOOK & ACT THE PART* series have been described as success and transformation 101.

She is a Fellow of the Chartered Institute of Personnel & Development (FCIPD), Fellow of the Australian Human Resources Institute (FAHRI), Fellow of the Institute of Leadership & Management (FInstLM), Member of the Society of Human Resources Management (SHRM) and Member of the Change Institute.

She is based in London, England with a strong penchant for travel and visiting new places. She is a food lover, ballet fanatic, passionate about music, art, theatre. She likes painting and drawing (for self-expression not selling but hey, you never know...), tennis, rugby, and of course fashion (the Pope is Catholic after all).

www.thepeoplealchemist.com
@PeopleAlchemist
instagram.com/lauramariani_author

NEW FICTION BY LAURA MARIANI

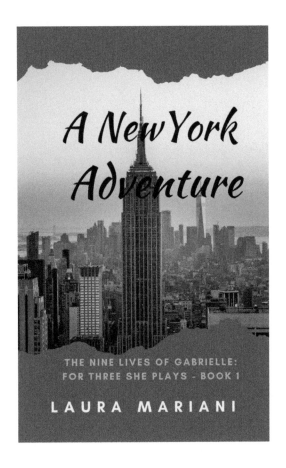

A New York Adventure

THE NINE LIVES OF GABRIELLE:
FOR THREE SHE PLAYS - BOOK 1

LAURA MARIANI

GABRIELLE STORY CONTINUE ...

THE NINE LIVES OF GABRIELLE:
FOR THREE SHE PLAYS - BOOK 2

SEARCHING FOR
Goren

LAURA MARIANI

NEW NON-FICTION BY LAURA MARIANI

ALSO BY LAURA MARIANI

Non-Fiction

STOP IT! It is all in your head

The RULE BOOK to Smash The infamous glass ceiling - For women & young women everywhere - personal transformation & success 101.

The Think, Look & Act The Part Series.

Think The Part

Upgrade your consciousness and mind-set. Make winning a key part of your life and business.

Look The Part

Upgrade your personal brand. Make presenting your unique Best Self a key part of your life and business.

Act The Part

A personal coach to act in spite of fear, right here, right now.

More non-fiction books and courses are coming soon. For new releases, giveaways and pre-release specials check www.thepeoplealchemist.com

You can also buy my books and courses directly from me at www.payhip.com/LauraMariani

ThePeopleAlchemist Press publishes self help, inspirational and transformational books, resources and products to help #TheWomanAlchemist in every woman to change her life / career and transmute any circumstance into gold, a bit like magic to **Unlock Ignite Transform.**

ISBN: 978-1-915501-06-6

*To whomever is trying to find themselves or their dreams right now;
look within. They are right there, waiting.*

PREFACE

Are you searching and never finding? The perfect place, perfect man, or woman, perfect career? Do you actually know what you are looking for in the first place?

To create what you want to have or achieve in the future implies and needs that you understand the here and.

Constantly chasing what you could have or whom you might meet means you ignore what exists all around you that already IS incredible.

Or, even worse, the incredible people who exist all around you.

Happiness and fulfilment already exist in your life, and they start with you. First and foremost.

Enjoy your life as it comes whilst working to be the best you.

The rest will take care of itself.

I t was the weekend, and Gabrielle reflected on the night out with Mr Wonderful. He had arranged dinner and Opera tickets to see Madam Butterfly, one of her favourite operas, to celebrate their meeting day.

Only a few months had passed since, and they had moved at the lighting speed. From meeting in the street to dinner/date to being in the same bubble in the last lockdown. And after that, he never left.

He seemed to remember every moment they had: their first meeting, first kiss, the first time they made love, their first weekend together. And celebrate it.

This amazing man in her life engaged in a more profound, authentic and emotional way than she had ever experienced. Fully, completely, emotionally and physically available.

Getting to know Gabrielle was like peeling an onion's multiple layers. She understood this about herself. She has had friends for over ten years who have never been to her house. Always kept something back. *Truly* opening up to anyone requires a level of intimacy she wasn't used to. And never liked. It required vulnerability.

The smell of coffee was permeating the room at the NoMad London hotel. He had thought of that too to continue the celebration into the weekend. Right in Covent Garden adjacent to the Royal Opera House, in the Bow Street Magistrates' Court Building. Splendid.

. . .

"Good morning, darling", he said, just back from the fitness centre. "I'm going in the shower. Want to join me?"

Dejavu.

"Obviously", she replied.

"How are you this morning?" Mr Wonderful enquired. His voice had an underlying worrying tone. Gabrielle had to do something to reassure him. Her mind wandered off and on all evening.

London - New York -London- New York. A round-the-world trip in one single evening. Better still, a round-the-world trip in her memories and back.

She felt so guilty.

New York had been an essential step in her life. The action that ultimately got her here today.

Becoming the woman she was today, albeit still a work in progress.

. . .

Three months were, she did not have the single-vision focus of her career but allowed herself to grow. In whichever direction. A last-minute decision to take a New York trip after a long-term relationship breakup turned out to be one of her best decisions to date. Besides giving her phone number to Mr Wonderful.

"Can I have your number?"
   he said, and then he called her straight away.

"You can't be missing me already; I'm still here,"
   Gabrielle told him, teasing.

"I just want to make sure I have the right number. And you now have mine too",
   grinning from side to side.
   "Are you sure I cannot convince you to have dinner with me tonight?".

That was for sure her best decision. But New York was a close second.

Three months in a different city, another country, led to further thinking. But, you take yourself wherever you go, and Gabrielle did just that initially and started a brief affair post-arrival that lasted almost two months.

But eventually, she came to her senses. She decided to REALLY explore the city. Not just the usual suspects like

Central Park, the Statue of Liberty or the Empire State Building but also, for example, the small breakfast cafe around the corner that served the biggest breakfast she had ever seen.

She walked in alone. Sat down with no distractions or barriers and ordered. What seemed like the smallest item on the menu.

"A cheese and ham omelette, please".

After a short time, the most humongous plate of food arrived at her table.

"Excuse me," she said. "I'm sorry, I think this is the wrong order. I asked for a cheese and ham omelette?"

"That's right," the server said. "That's it, honey".

The plate was overflowing. God knows how many eggs were used; probably a whole battery of hens was at work here. And there were chips, bread slices, and so on.

Gabrielle struggled to finish the omelette itself and left all the "garnish" behind.

"What's wrong, honey?"

the server looked worried.

"Was there something wrong with the food? You left the majority behind ... Do you want to take it away?"

"Good Lord, no", Gabrielle was thinking. "Far more carbs than I have ever seen in my life".

"I wasn't that hungry; it was delicious, thank you,"
    she said aloud and made sure she left a generous tip behind.

She also learned to wander the various neighbourhoods; slow and purposeful walks to get to know the area, even better, people. She was not afraid to ask questions and be seen as the tourist that she actually was. Or someone just learning. Shocking.

She stopped seeing the VP around her second month in New York and started to go out. Alone. Dinners. Theatres.

She even booked herself in a writers' conference, something she had always wanted to do.

The VP didn't take it very well. Not that he ever wanted to pursue a long-distance relationship, but he was at least counting on keeping the relationship going until at least she was departing.

· · ·

At the writers' conference, she met many people, most Americans, a mix of professional, semi-professional, amateurs and wanna-be writers. All extraordinarily nice and friendly. All were extremely surprised but supportive of her first trip alone.

"You are here alone?"

"Yes, I am. I am not visiting anybody. And I had nothing planned, nowhere specific to go when I arrived" proud moment.

Gabrielle felt great about herself now. Even better knowing that everyone recognised she had been courageous. They didn't realise that the scariest part of her trip had been walking into a restaurant for dinner alone. For the first time ever.

Much harder than travelling across the world. The inner battles are always the hardest and the most satisfying when you win.

And the second most challenging thing was the realisation that the men she had dated, their red flags, were her red flags. They just carried them around for her. And she had decided it was time to put them down, once and for all.

All the men she dated were the same man.
     They were HER.

. . .

They were exactly right for her each time because they were safe and presented no real risk of ultimately getting hurt.

Gabrielle realised she had been committed to not committing.
"That's a commitment for you," she thought, smiling.

Slowly but surely, in the same New York where she lived the fantasy of pursuing Detective Goren, she slowly broke her shackles.

"I'm good darling, Terrific. Never better,"
she said, smiling. "I think I owe you an apology".

"No, you don't. I just want to know you are ok, that we are ok".

"Absolutely", she said." So, let's have that shower and then a chat?"

"It's not one of those 'We need to talk' moments, right?"
Mr Wonderful asked.

"No, no, no …."

"Vicar of Dibley?" he asked, smiling.

. . .

"No, no, YES ... no", she replied, smiling.

After a long, steamy shower, they went for a walk and just like that, Gabrielle started talking.

For the first time, really talking: she told him about New York, the why, the when and the how. She told him everything.

Ok, not E-V-E-R-Y-T-H-I-N-G.

She omitted the chasing Vincent D'Onofrio/Goren around NYC like a crazy person.

"This onion needs to keep some layers,"
    she thought. At least for now.

And as their day was ending, her shackles were falling even more, and Gabrielle was finally tasting freedom.

Freedom is an elusive concept.

Some men hold themselves prisoner even when they have the power to do as they please and go where they choose, while others are free in their hearts, even as shackles restrain them.

-- Brian Herbert

AFTERWORD

Vulnerability is where courage and fear meet. It is awkward and scary, but it is also freedom and liberation.

Being uniquely you: embracing your imperfections and daring to be vulnerable, engaging fully and openly with the world around you, being open despite knowing it might hurt you, feeling love, belonging and joy.

It feels a bit like going out there without makeup, with no armour hoping the real you isn't too disappointing. And still feeling worthy.

Ouch! I know, it sound scary.

But realise that you ARE worthy. Right here, right now. Perfectly imperfect and absolutely fabulous.

Laura xxx

DISCLAIMER

Tasting Freedom is a work of fiction.

Although its form is that of an autobiography, it is not one.

With the exception of public places, any resemblance to persons living or dead is coincidental. Space and time have been rearranged to suit the convenience of the book, memory has its own story to tell.

The opinions expressed are those of the characters and should not be confused with the author's.

AUTHOR'S NOTE

Thank you so much for reading *Tasting Freedom.*

I hope you enjoyed this novella as an escapist story, but perhaps you also glimpsed something beneath as you read. A review would be much appreciated as it helps other readers discover the story. Thanks.

If you sign up for my newsletter you'll be notified of give-aways, new releases and receive personal updates from behind the scenes of my business and books.

Go to www.thepeoplealchemist.com to get started.

Places in the book

I have set the story in real places in London and New York - find out more about them or perhaps, go and visit:

- Central Park
- Empire State Building
- NoMad London
- Royal Opera House, London
- The New York Public Library
- The Statue of Liberty

- Times Square
- TownePlace Suites, Manhattan / Times Square
- NYC West Village

Bibliography

I read a lot of books as part of my research. Some of them together with other references include:

Psycho-Cybernetics - **Maxwell Maltz**
The Complete Reader - **Neville Goddard**

The Vicar of Dibley - British sitcom starring Dawn French as the Vicar of the rural parish of Dibley, It made its debut in 1994.

Printed in Great Britain
by Amazon